Noddy
Tidies Toyland

Collins

An Imprint of HarperCollins*Publishers*

NODDY

CLOCKWORK MOUSE

BIG-EARS

TESSIE BEAR

GOBBO

MARTH

MR PLOD

MASTER TUBBY BEAR

ONKEY

SLY

MR WOBBLY MAN

BUMPY DOG

It was a blustery morning in Toyland . . .

Noddy was busy picking up all the rubbish that had blown into his garden.

"A toffee paper...and another..." he muttered to himself rather crossly.

There seemed to be toffee wrappers blowing about everywhere. One even floated down and stuck on Noddy's nose! *Where* were all these sticky wrappers coming from?

The toffee wrappers were still blowing into the garden. Noddy peered over the fence.

Ah, *that's* where the toffee wrappers were coming from! Noddy might have guessed...

It was that naughty Master Tubby not caring one little bit about all the mess he was making!

"Master Tubby!" shouted Noddy crossly. "Whatever are you doing?"

"I'm eating toffees, of course," Master Tubby replied, munching happily.

"Yes – and then letting all the wrappers blow into my garden!" Noddy exclaimed.

Noddy was very stern with Master Tubby, telling him it was wrong to drop sweet wrappers. On a windy day like this, they would blow all over Toyland!

Noddy was not the only one in Toyland who was getting annoyed about all the rubbish.

Dinah Doll was bothered about it too, especially when Mr Plod joked about the rubbish on her stall.

"I'm not selling rubbish," she complained to Mr Plod, "I'm keeping my stall tidy. Some toys are very careless."

Dinah Doll asked Mr Plod to investigate the cause of all this rubbish.

"Oh, I've got much more important things to do than stop people dropping rubbish," Mr Plod huffed crossly.

"Then you won't mind about your shoe," Dinah Doll told him.

"What about my shoe?" Mr Plod asked, looking down. He saw that there were some sweet wrappers stuck to it!

Mr Plod tried to get rid of the sweet wrappers by peeling them off his shoe. But the wrappers just stuck to his hands instead!

"Oh, this is an outrage!" he cried as the sweet wrappers stuck first to one hand, then the other. "Oh...oh bother. It is a very serious offence to make a policeman become all sticky."

Rubbish was causing trouble elsewhere in Toyland.

A milk bottle rolled along the pavement and knocked into Jumbo.

"Ouch!" he cried as he fell heavily to the ground.

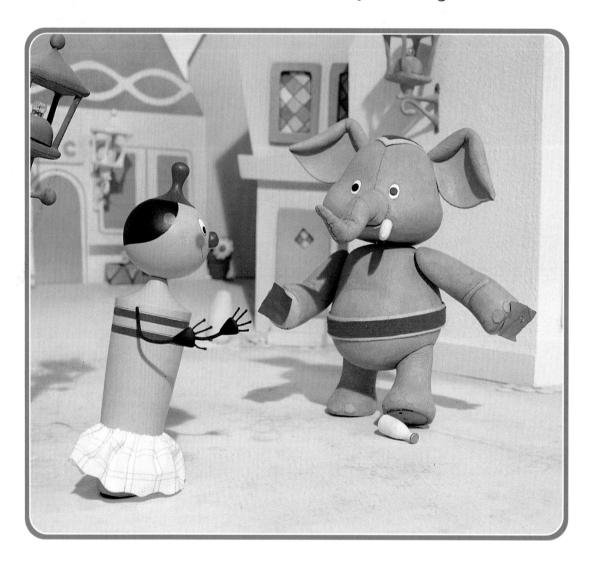

In another part of Toyland, Clockwork Clown was also heading for a fall.

"Aren't his tricks clever!" Martha Monkey cried as she watched with admiration.

Clockwork Mouse walked away, however, saying he had seen all Clockwork Clown's tricks before.

Oh, do watch that banana skin, Clockwork Clown!

Oh dear, it was too late!

Clockwork Clown slipped on the banana skin and went somersaulting all over the place.

"What a pity Clockwork Mouse went away!" Martha Monkey exclaimed, clapping excitedly. "Clockwork Clown has never done a trick like that before!"

People just seemed to be leaving all sorts of rubbish today.

"I've never seen such a hideous wheelbarrow in all my life!" Sammy Sailor moaned as he struggled to push it along.

Suddenly, a wobbly wheel came right off Sammy Sailor's wheelbarrow, causing it to crash to the ground.
CRASH!

"Oh that's useless, it's not worth mending."

So, after unloading it, he left the wheelbarrow –
right where it was!

Even the countryside seemed to be full of rubbish and litter.

Mr Sparks was taking Miss Pink Cat for a nice relaxing drive in his car.

They were having such an enjoyable time...

But then a lollipop wrapper blew into Mr Sparks' face, covering his eyes.

"Help! Help!" Mr Sparks cried. "I can't see a thing!"

Both Mr Sparks and Miss Pink Cat gasped as the car veered all over the road.

"Look out! The stream!" Miss Pink Cat shrieked as the car spun this way and that.

"What stream?" Mr Sparks cried, still not able to see properly.

"This stream!" Miss Pink Cat declared crossly after the car had skidded off the road and plunged into the water.

Mr Sparks finally managed to remove the sticky lollipop wrapper from his face.

"Oh yes, I see the stream now," he said glumly.

Noddy, Jumbo and Mr Wobbly Man thought they had
found some rubbish too.

"What a sight!" gasped Mr Wobbly Man as they stared
in horror at the ugly statue outside Miss Pink Cat's
house. It was a statue of Miss Pink Cat herself!

"It spoils Toyland!" declared Noddy.

Just at that moment, Miss Pink Cat arrived, still soaking wet. She looked just as much a sight as her statue!

"Whatever's the matter, Miss Pink Cat?" Mr Wobbly Man asked.

"Lollipop wrappers," she replied furiously. "They blew over Mr Sparks' eyes and he crashed into the stream!"

Miss Pink Cat decided that it was time something was done about all the rubbish in Toyland.

"What we need," she said, "is to get everyone picking up rubbish."

"I will give a reward," she announced. "Ten sixpences for the toy who collects the most rubbish!"

Noddy raced off in his car to find some rubbish.
He really wanted to win that reward!

"There's some rubbish!" he cried suddenly, braking to
a halt. "A great big heap of rubbish!"

It was Sammy Sailor's broken wheelbarrow!

Noddy asked Mr Noah if he would help him lift the wheelbarrow on to his car.

Mr Noah was only too pleased to help because the wheelbarrow was blocking his way.

"One, two, three...lift!" Noddy cried.

All the other toys had been collecting rubbish as well.

They took their rubbish to Market Square where Mr Plod told them how pleased he was.

"I'm pleased to announce that all the rubbish has now been removed from Toyland!" he said.

Mr Plod then proudly revealed a new addition to
Toyland – its first ever rubbish bin!

"Now, I would like you all to place the rubbish you
have collected into this bin," he declared.

The very first toy to step up to the rubbish bin was
Master Tubby.

Mr Plod showed him how to use the bin.

"Well done!" everyone cheered.

Master Tubby was so pleased with himself!

Now all the other toys lined up for the rubbish
bin, dropping in all the rubbish they had collected.

Miss Pink Cat kept a careful note of what each toy
dropped in so she could work out who had won the
reward.

Miss Pink Cat was just about to announce who had won the reward when Noddy arrived in his car.

But when she saw the broken wheelbarrow on Noddy's car, Miss Pink Cat quickly changed her mind.

She decided that the toy who most deserved the reward was quite definitely...Noddy!

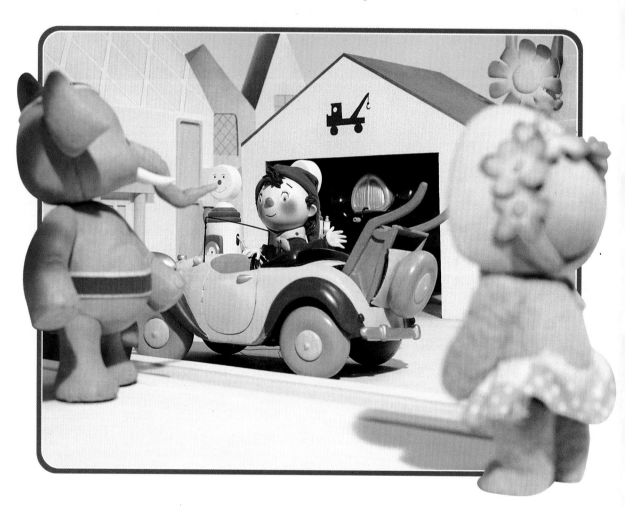

"The winner of ten sixpences is Noddy!" Miss Pink Cat announced as she presented him with the reward.

Everyone clapped and cheered.

Although Noddy was a little shy about it all, he couldn't hide his delight!

So Toyland was nice and clean again.
All thanks to Miss Pink Cat and her clever idea!
    Indeed, she even offered to make Toyland look nicer still – by removing that horrible statue of herself from in front of her house!

This edition first published in Great Britain by HarperCollins Publishers Ltd in 2000

1 3 5 7 9 10 8 6 4 2

Copyright © 1999 Enid Blyton Ltd. Enid Blyton's signature mark and the words
"NODDY" and "TOYLAND" are Registered Trade Marks of Enid Blyton Ltd.
For further information on Enid Blyton please contact www.blyton.com

ISBN: 0 00 136179 1

Reproduction by Graphic Studio S.r.l. Verona
Printed in Italy by Garzanti Verga S.r.l.

MORE NODDY BOOKS FOR YOU TO ENJOY

Noddy and the Artists

Noddy and the Bouncing Ball

Noddy and the Goblins

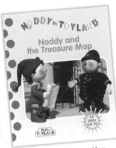

Noddy and the Treasure Map

Noddy and the Singing Bush

Noddy and the Noisy Drum

Noddy is Caught in a Storm

Noddy and the Driving Lesson

Noddy is Far Too Busy

Noddy and the Magic Watch

Noddy the Nurse

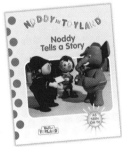

Noddy Tells a Story